1993

To
my Dearest Friend
Barbara —

May the joy
Christmas always [bring?]
your heart — and [may?]
"Santa" always bring [a?]
smile to your lips —
Your friendship is
dearly treasured —
Love always
Pat

Memories
of Santa
Collection™

Memories of Santa Collection™

by
Don Warning

Christmas Reproductions Inc., New York

Published by Christmas Reproductions, Inc.
P.O. Box 1536, New York, NY 10156-0607

Printed in the British Crown Colony of Hong Kong

First Edition

Photography by Susan Cook

CONTENTS

CONTENTS

REFACE

Although this book was intended to be a chronological history of the Santas in the Memories of Santa Collection, it developed into the Life and Legend of the early St. Nicholas to the current day Santa Claus.

The fact that the Memories of Santa Collection of forty-four Santas was created before this book was written was, I believe, a necessity.

The creation of the three dimensional Santas inspired by antique art and legends provided me with the vehicle necessary to communicate the historical events, customs, and traditions I thought people would like to know about America's most loved and treasured personality, Santa Claus.

Throughout the design and development of each of the Santas in the collection and the research required to write the history and legends, I could see a story evolving about the early St. Nicholas, his travels through Europe, England, the Middle-East, and finally to America where Santa was and is immortalized as our national hero.

During Santa's evolution through the ages, and in his travels from country to country, each area's traditions and customs shaped his persona somewhat, yet at the same time he had a dramatic effect on countries, Kings of countries, families, and individuals throughout the world.

Santa has survived the ages.
He is truly a "classic" in our culture.

ST. NICK
(by T.C. Boyd)

AMERICA
CIRCA 1840

This St. Nick was inspired by a series of woodcuts created by Theodore C. Boyd. The woodcuts were used to illustrate the first printing as a separate book of the classic American poem, "A Visit From St. Nicholas" by Clement C. Moore.

The natty St. Nick's clothing shows the early Dutch influence of New Amsterdam with his Dutch pipe, buckle shoes,and Knickerbockers, later known as knickers. Knickerbockers was the name given to the early Dutch settlers in New Amsterdam by Washington Irving in his famous book of 1809,"Knickerbockers History of New York."

In the Boyd wood-cut reproduction below you can see he must have taken "tiny reindeer" from Moore's poem literally. Notice the woodcut has only seven reindeer instead of Clement C. Moore's famous eight.

Introduced 1993

A Visit from St. Nicholas

WEIHNACHTSMAN

GERMANY
CIRCA 1850

This 1850 Weihnachtsman (Christmas Man) was inspired by an antique chocolate mold, similar to the one pictured below.

Normally his bucket was filled with ashes and he would be called Ashenclos (Nicholas with Ashes for bad boys and girls). However, the creator of this figure elected to fill the bucket with red apples and a typical German Christmas heart-shaped cookie (for good little boys and girls).

Note the clusters of three tiny gold balls sprinkled over his green robe. These three balls are symbolic of the three bags of gold St. Nicholas lowered into the window in the home of a needy family. (Refer to the legend of SINT NIKLAES circa 1910)

This piece was introduced by Christmas Reproductions, Inc. in 1983 as a limited edition (1850A), and the design was altered in 1984 to protect the integrity of the first edition. The apple bucket was moved from his left side to his right side for subsequent production (1850B).

1850A Introduced 1983	Retired 1984
1850B Introduced 1984	Retired 1987

1870 Chocolate Mold Catalogue
ANTON REICHE
DRESDEN GERMANY

ᒐANTA CLAUS
(by Charles G. Bush)

AMERICA
CIRCA 1867

This Memories of Santa Collection figure was inspired by a drawing published in the December 28, 1867 issue of Harpers Weekly Magazine, shown below, along with other art of this period. It was done by the artist Charles G. Bush.

Here he is dressed in a costume similar to one of Thomas Nast's drawings and sports a riding crop and a large bag full of toys.

His loose britches, gathered at the knees were called Knickerbockers (later shortened to Knickers). DIEDRICH KNICKERBOCKER was the pen-name used by Washington Irving for his famous book written in 1809, "History of New York." This was a satirical work about Knickerbocker men, descendants of New York's Dutch settlers.

It was in "History of New York" that Irving wrote a great deal about St. Nicholas, which is said to have had an influence on Clement Moore when he wrote "A Visit from St. Nicholas."

Introduced 1991

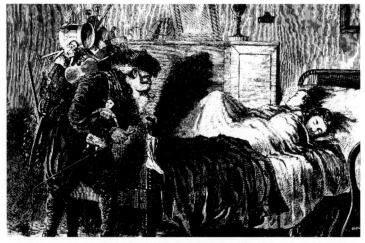

SANTA CLAUS - Drawn by Charles G. Bush
Harpers Weekly
December 28, 1897

1867

SANTA CLAUS
(by Thomas Nast)

AMERICA
CIRCA 1872

Thomas Nast's first Santa appeared on the cover of Harpers Weekly newspaper January 3, 1863. The Nast Santa drawings appeared in the holiday issues of Harpers Weekly until 1866. Although he was a political cartoonist he is best remembered for his drawings of Santa Claus. You will note that the buckled boots and clay pipe in the Nast Santa were inspired by early Dutch styles in New Amsterdam.

Nast was also responsible for the red Santa suit. When he was approached by McLoughlin Brothers, publishers of the first children's book to use the newly discovered color-printing process, he had a problem. His earlier works were done only in black ink for Harpers Weekly which would not translate immediately into the new colorful illustrations, so Nast made the Santa suit bright red trimmed with white ermine fur.

Thomas Nast was largely responsible for transforming the earlier St. Nicholas to the American Santa Claus.

Introduced 1985   Retired 1992

Harpers Weekly
January 3, 1874

SHENCLOS

(St. Nicholas carrying bucket of Ashes)

GERMANY
CIRCA 1880

In Germany began the custom of gift giving on Christmas Day, December 25th, instead of the Eve of St. Nicholas Day, December 5th. It was there that St. Nick's bishop-like robes changed to simpler ones.

He is carrying only the traditional evergreen Christmas tree and a bucket of ashes. St. Nicholas carrying ashes (for bad little girls and boys) was called Ashenclos.

This Ashenclos was modeled after a casting from an antique German chocolate mold, (c. 1880), then resculpted, the Christmas tree was added, and then of course the figured was painted.

Introduced by Christmas Reproductions, Inc. in 1983 as a limited edition (1880A), the design of this piece was altered in 1984 to protect the integrity of the first edition by switching the location of the ash bucket from the left side of the figure to the right side (1880B).

1880A Introduced 1983   Retired 1984

1880B Introduced 1984   Retired 1987

BUTLER BROS. CATALOGUE 1932

$\mathcal{K}$RIS KRINGLE
ST. NICHOLAS

PENNSYLVANIA, USA
CIRCA 1885

This Kris Kringle figure was inspired by Christmas cards of the late 1800's.

The name Kris Kringle was given to St. Nicholas by the Pennsylvania Dutch settlers. Just as the term for "German," "Deutch," was colloquialized to "Dutch" in the Pennsylvania colony, the name CHRISTKINDL was also colloquialized later to become KRIS KRINGLE.

In the seventeenth century the northern Germans adopted the name CHRISTKINDL (Christ Child) for their gift-giver, thus subjugating St. Nicholas to the simply robed Pelze-Nicol. In the early 1800's the German immigrants came to Pennsylvania with their Christmas customs of Christmas trees and Christkindl. Through intermarriage with the English and others the original meaning was lost and KRIS KRINGLE became synonymous with Santa Claus.

Introduced 1985   Retired 1992

CHRISTKINDL

$\mathcal{F}$ATHER CHRISTMAS
(Wassailing)

ENGLAND
CIRCA 1888

The Wassailing Father Christmas was released in 1988 during the 100th anniversary year of the publication of the art which inspired it. The drawings appeared in Punch Magazine in England dated December 29, 1888.

Father Christmas is carrying a wassail bowl with apples floating on top and his hood is crowned with the traditional holly wreath.

The old English custom of Wassailing began in the middle ages when the English would wassail (to toast) their neighbors, their fruit trees and their oxen to a long, healthy and productive life.

Later the poorer folks would wassail their masters and the more well-to-do by first singing Christmas carols and then wassailing with them in hopes of a few pence reward.

This was the beginning of Christmas caroling, and Father Christmas or St. Nicholas added his contribution to this "Good will to all men" festivity.

Introduced 1988

∫T. NICHOLAS

with Doll

GERMANY
CIRCA 1889

Beautiful antique German chromolithographs were the inspirations for creating this green-suited St. Nicholas with a doll in his outstretched hand.

Chromolithographs are also known as chromos, die-cuts, or scraps. They were die-cut, usually embossed, and sometimes gilded. The process of lithography was invented in Germany in 1798. This process printed a single color by the use of stone plates. Chromolithography or color-lithography was invented in 1837. Steel plates were used in this operation. The colored image to be printed was separated into its constituent colors and the required number of plates were prepared according to the number of colors to be printed. Sometimes as many as twenty-six colors were done. This was the first form of any color printing process.

Chromos were a rage in Victorian times, up to the turn of the century. Families would sit in their parlours and create "scrap" books. They were also used on greeting cards, cookies, cakes, and Christmas ornaments.

In 1989 Christmas Reproductions, Inc. introduced a fine porcelain bisque limited edition as a centennial reproduction of the 1889 art. In this piece St. Nicholas is holding the doll beside a sleeping Victorian girl.

Introduced 1990

$\mathscr{P}$ELZE-NICOL
(Fur Clad Nicholas)

GERMANY
CIRCA 1890

In Northern Germany the gift-giving day was changed from St. Nicholas Day to Christmas Day. Like Ashenclos c. 1880, the Germans simplified St. Nicholas' garments and appearance and he reappeared as Pelze-Nicol or Fur Clad Nicholas.

This particular Pelze-Nicol was cast from an original antique chocolate mold (c. 1890), then resculpted, at which time the kitten and clown (or doll) were added.

Introduced by Christmas Reproductions in 1983 as a limited edition (1890A), the design of this piece was altered in 1984 to protect the integrity of the first edition by changing the doll carried under his right arm to a clown (1890).

1890A Introduced 1983	Retired 1984
1890B Introduced 1984	Retired 1987

*S*ANTA CLAUS

AMERICA
CIRCA 1890

This dashing Santa graced the cover of PUCK magazine for December 3, 1890. It was entitled "Christmas Puck." The picture shows Santa descending the steps of the Puck Building to his waiting sleigh and reindeer. On the coachman's seat of the elaborately carved sleigh, holding the reigns for Santa, is the young mascot for PUCK Magazine dressed in top hat and tails.

The Puck Building still stands today in lower Manhattan with the Puck mascot at the entrance represented in stone.

Introduced 1990

CHRISTMAS PUCK MAGAZINE
December 3, 1890

WEIHNACHTSMAN
(Christmas Man)

GERMANY
CIRCA 1893

This very typical German St. Nicholas called Weihnachtsman·or Christmas Man was inspired by several antique German Christmas cards. On one of the cards was printed, "FROLICHE WEIHNACHTEN" which means Happy Christmas!

Notice he is delivering a Christmas tree already decorated with colored ball ornaments. These balls probably represent the round hand-blown glass ornaments invented in Laucha, Germany in the 1840's.

Introduced 1992

$\mathcal{N}$IKLO
(St. Nicholas)

AUSTRIA
CIRCA 1894

This Austrian St. Nicholas (NIKLO), clad in a gold robe trimmed with fur, is smoking a Tyrolean pipe and carrying a backpack and hiking staff. In addition to toys in his backpack, he is also carrying his mountain climbing tools. He was inspired by antique Chromolithograph post cards. The artist is unknown.

In creating this Austrian NIKLO one can see how the artist added typical Austrian artifacts and traditions to the figure. Keeping in mind that St. Nicholas/Santa travels through Europe, the Middle East, England and America, and considering the influence of all the different customs and traditions, it is no wonder there are so many different Santas in the Memories of Santa Collection™.

Introduced 1987

TYROLEAN PIPE
Chocolate Mold
c. 1870 DRESDEN, GERMANY

KRIS KRINGLE

ST. NICHOLAS

PENNSYLVANIA, U.S.A.
CIRCA 1895

This Kris Kringle was inspired by several original chromolithograph Post Cards, one of which was postmarked 1895.

Here he dons a more ecclesiastical outer garment and an undergarment decorated with gold stars, symbolic of the Nativity.

As described in the legend of the 1885 Santa, this 1895 Kris Kringle was also named as a result of the colloquialization of the word Christkindl to Kris Kringle in the Pennsylvania Dutch country. There Kris Kringle was used synonymously with Santa Claus.

Introduced 1984   Retired 1987

E. FERRETT & CO.
PHILADELPHIA
1845.

*This is one of the earliest
printings of the name KRISS (KRIS) KRINGLE*

$\mathcal{J}$T. NICHOLAS

CZECHOSLOVAKIA
CIRCA 1896

This Nicholas from Czechoslovakia is very different from most European or American versions.

To our eyes he appears very exotic in his mulicolored Byzantine style garments. The little doll is dressed in colors similar to Nicholas'. She wears a festive native costume.

The basket of apples seems to be the only element he possesses in common with other Santas in the collection.

One of the Christmas post cards which influenced this design was inscribed "VESELE VANOCE," meaning "Joyful Night!" in the Czechoslovakian language.

Introduced 1992

$\mathcal{S}$T. NICHOLAS

CZECHOSLOVAKIA
CIRCA 1897

This Czechoslovakian version of St. Nicholas looks very frigid with icicles hanging from his headgear. Perhaps he has come near the end of his appointed rounds.

Although the nutcracker and doll hanging from his belt are toys for a good boy and girl, the rabbit at his feet is not a toy but a real one from the woods who came to be near the benevolent St. Nicholas, friend to animals as well as children.

Rabbits were often part of the Christmas scene in Europe as well as being prevalent at Eastertime.

Introduced 1987

THE LITTLE ABC BOOK
McLoughlin Bros.
New York 1884

AMERICA
CIRCA 1898

In the evolution of the European St. Nicholas to the current day Santa many artists were commissioned to illustrate Santa Claus. Any new invention or trend was often incorporated with the Santa figure, such as dirigibles, airplanes, trucks, and cars.

With the invention of the telephone, hundreds of Santas were drawn with Santa using each new instrument as it appeared on the market. This 1898 Santa is shown using the new "Desk Set" telephone which was first introduced in 1897.

One illustration in Harper's Weekly shows a little girl talking on the phone to Santa, saying, "Hello Santa Claus!" and Santa replies, "Hello, Little One!" This was the inspiration for the title above.

Introduced 1993

"HELLO SANTA CLAUS"

SANTA CLAUS

R. Tuck & Sons

USA
CIRCA 1899

An illustration for the cover of a "Night Before Christmas" book containing Clement C. Moore's beloved poem was influential in the design of this Santa Claus.

This turn of the century book was produced by Raphael Tuck and Sons Co. Ltd. of London and New York, who were the leading publishers of popular works at that time.

An original copy of this "Night Before Christmas" is in the Christmas antique collection of Don Warning.

Introduced 1991

ꞘINT NIKLAES

(St. Nicholas)

BELGIUM
CIRCA 1900

The Memories of Santa collectible pictured here was inspired by Christmas post cards actually printed in Belgium. The robe, as you can see, was a delicate blue trimmed with white fur and on one card was sprinkled with mica glitter. A blue robed St. Nicholas was often depicted in Belgium and France. Toys for good boys and girls hang from his belt and backpack.

On the front of one lithographed post card was imprinted BONNE ANNEE which means "A Good Year!"

Introduced 1988

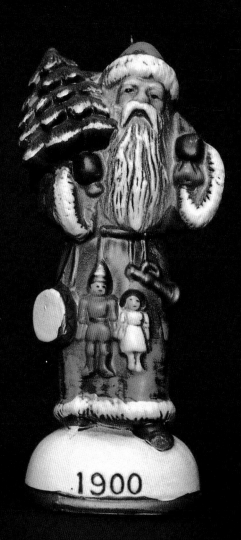

PELZE-NICOL
(Fur-clad Nicholas)

GERMANY
CIRCA 1901

The Pelze-Nicol or Fur-clad St. Nicholas originated in Germany. The antique post card which inspired it was an embossed chromolithograph. Chromolithography also originated in Germany in the mid 1800's. Chromolithography was the first form of color reproduction.

The little black doll in his pocket was most probably a miniature toy version of Swarte Peter or Black Peter, a Moorish boy in native dress who accompanied St. Nicholas on his journey to visit all the little boys and girls.

Below is Thomas Nast's American version of a Pelze-Nicol (fur-clad Santa) that he had known as a child in Germany where he was born in 1840.

Introduced 1987

ᵖERE NOEL
(Father Christmas)

FRANCE
CIRCA 1902

In his unique brown robe Pere Noel is unloading his bag full of toys and fruits for the good boys and girls.

It was in France, in the early twelfth century, that the custom of gift giving on the feast day of St. Nicholas, December 6th, originated.

The French nuns would leave gifts of fruits, nuts and oranges on the doorsteps of poor families with children. The fruits and nuts were from Spain and were a luxury the poor families could not afford. The custom spread throughout Europe to both rich and poor, and finally evolved into the custom of filling stockings with goodies on the eve of the feast day, December 5th.

Introduced 1988

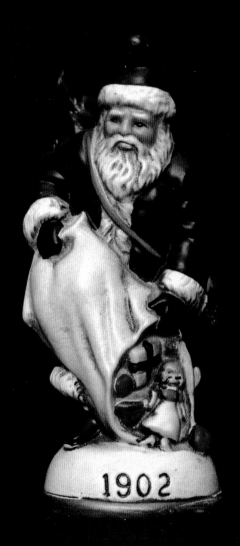

FATHER CHRISTMAS

RUSSIA
CIRCA 1903

1903 Father Christmas from Russia was inspired by an early 20th century cotton batting figure. Under the base was a label with cyrillic lettering, indicating its Russian origin.

Before the 1917 Revolution, the old Russian St. Nicholas was known as Father Christmas. After the Revolution he was called Ded Moroz (Grandfather Frost), the Russian Spirit of Winter who brings gifts to the children on Christmas Day.

Both figures were very similar in appearance, each in a long robe with a huge fur collar to brave the Russian winters, and the flat-crowned hat, traditionally Russian.

Introduced 1989   Retired 1993

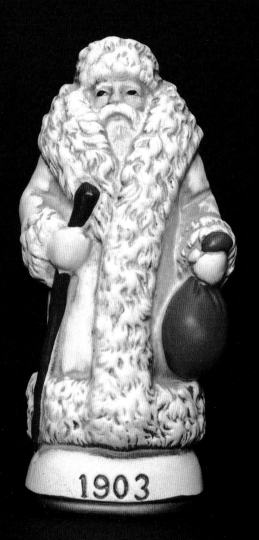

ST. NICHOLAS

GERMANY
CIRCA 1904

Many German artists painted St. Nicholas during this period. This example is somewhat special in that his hat is a different color (blue) from his robe (red). Usually the German St. Nicholas had the hat or hood in a color matching the robe.

This St. Nicholas was only on the market for two years, 1989 through 1990, and retired January 1, 1991. This means fewer were produced and distributed, and therefore fewer are in circulation in the secondary market.

Introduced 1989   Retired 1991

ℱATHER CHRISTMAS

ENGLAND
CIRCA 1905

In England, the role of St. Nicholas was filled by Father Christmas. He was usually clad in a red robe with white trim and wore a white beard.

Father Christmas did not take part in the feasting of the Twelve Days of Christmas until Christmas Day, which was January sixth of the old calendar. On this day he rode a donkey from house to house and from feast to feast.

This Father Christmas was inspired by an original chromolithograph post card. Notice the Union Jack in his shoulder bag.

Introduced 1984   Retired 1990

ST. NICHOLAS

BAVARIA
CIRCA 1906

This handsome Bavarian St. Nicholas, dressed in a flowing robe, sporting a fine leather shoulder bag, and laden with toys is a result of the fine quality of art used for the publishing of chromolithograph post cards which flourished at that time.

The publishers would commission the finest artists to do series of post cards, usually in sets of four. From one of these series of St. Nicholas post cards was created a composite for the Circa 1906 Bavarian Nicholas.

Introduced 1987

SINTERKLASS

HOLLAND
CIRCA 1907

In Holland, the Dutch name for St. Nicholas is Sinterklass. Like the Northern Germans, the Dutch also had a helper for Sinterklass called Black Peter or SWARTE PIET. He carried switches along with the bag of gifts. His face was stained black and he wore a colorful Moorish costume from Spain. The costume was in commemoration of the ending of the war between Spain and Holland.

In 1621 when the Dutch settled in New Amsterdam, they, of course, brought along their tradition of celebrating the feast Day of Sinterklass, December 6th. Later in 1664, the British took over New Amsterdam and renamed it New York. With the intermingling of the British and Dutch children, Sinterklass was often called SANCTE CLAUS and finally SANTA CLAUS.

The Dutch celebrated St. Nick's Day on December 6th and the English celebrated Christmas in early January. Several generations later both groups agreed to change the date for celebrating Christmas to December 25th.

Introduced 1986   Retired 1991

December
25

ℬULLER CLOS

NORTHERN GERMANY
CIRCA 1908

In some regions of Germany St. Nicholas is called Buller Clos (Nicholas with Bells). Here is another example of the evolving of St. Nicholas' ecclesiastical robes into more simple ones and the changing of the gift-giving day to Christmas instead of St. Nicholas Day, December 6.

Like Pelze-Nicol and Ashenclos, Buller Clos has plain garments but the addition of the new silver bells suggests a social need for a more ornate decorative personage to depict the illustrious tradition of this time-tested personality.

Chromolithograph post cards were the inspiration for Buller Clos.

Introduced 1986   Retired 1991

 WEIHNACHTSMAN

SOUTHERN GERMANY
CIRCA 1909

In northern Europe St. Nicholas had helpers or servants, such as Swarte Piet or Black Peter of Holland, or Knecht Ruprecht and Krampas of Northern Germany (see below). These helpers were very mean looking and frightening to the children and often threatened them with their switches. The good St. Nick would follow along, showing kindness to the children and giving them presents.

In other parts of Germany St. Nicholas made his visits to the children without a helper and was known as Weihnachtsman or Christmas Man. The Weihnachtsman here is illustrated in a green fur-trimmed robe and hat, wielding a walking stick.

The sculpture was inspired by an original antique chromolithograph post card.

Introduced 1985   Retired 1992

Knecht Ruprecht.

Sint Niklaes

Belgium
CIRCA 1910

This Sint Niklaes (St. Nicholas) of Belgium was sculpted using die cut chromolithographs as inspiration. Chromolithography, invented in 1830 in Germany, was the first form of color reproduction prior to color printing.

Here, Sint Niklaes is holding the crooked staff which was fashioned after St. Joseph's shepherd's staff.

The gold ball in the right hand is symbolic of the gift of three bags of gold St. Nicklaes gave to a family in need.

St. Niklaes later became the patron saint of countries, tradesman and occupations such as pawnbrokers and bankers. The pawnbrokers eventually adopted the three gold balls as the sign in front of their shops up through the early twentieth century.

Introduced 1985   Retired 1992

ST. NICHOLAS

GERMANY
CIRCA 1911

This German St. Nicholas, whose bag of toys is tied on a tree branch, has a leather satchel over his shoulder and is wearing a holly wreath over his hood.

Holly, like the Christmas tree, plays a part in ancient lore in the belief that evergreens possess magical powers to thrive all year round. An ancient Roman custom was to bring evergreens into the house in order to perpetuate life in the new year. All evergreens were held in high regard, particularly the holly branches, whose berries were revered as a symbol of fertility.

In northern Europe the custom continued and evergreens were some-times shaped into the circular sun-symbol configuration of the holly wreath.

Introduced 1989   Retired 1993

$\mathcal{U}$NCLE SAM SANTA

USA
CIRCA 1912

The Uncle Sam, or Stars and Stripes Santa was first conceived by Thomas Nast.

Being a political cartoonist, Nast created the first Stars and Stripes Santa in 1863 for the cover of Harpers Weekly.

The red, white and blue Santa called the Uncle Sam Santa was named after a supplier of provisions to United States troops. Their packages were all labeled US and the troops created the nickname Uncle Sam.

The Uncle Sam Santa, c. 1912, was inspired by post cards in a series of four illustrating Uncle Sam Santas.

Introduced 1986   Retired 1991

THOMAS NAST'S
FIRST SANTA CLAUS
January 3, 1863

Tomta

SWEDEN
CIRCA 1913

TOMTA or JULTOMTEN are the Swedish names for Santa Claus. The Memories of Santa Collection™ circa 1913 version was inspired by several post cards of this era. The later Jultomtens are more whimsical and elf-like.

Two other Scandinavian countries have similar names: JULESVENN from Norway, and JULNISSE from Denmark.

Jultomten often rides a goat named JULBOCK. This animal has pagan origins, being modeled after the goat of Thor that pulled its master's chariot. Straw goats of many sizes are sold at Christmas time in Sweden.

Introduced 1991

THE LITTLE ABC BOOK
McLoughlin Bros.
1884

$\mathcal{V}$IVE ST. NICOLAS

BELGIUM
CIRCA 1914

This St. Nicolas figure was inspired by several Belgian post cards dated 1910 to 1922.

One of the cards was postmarked 1914, the year of the beginning of World War I. The children in this card were wearing sailor-type clothing which reflected the style of the time. The front of the post card bears the greeting VIVE ST. NICOLAS.

St. Nicolas was often dressed in a brown furry robe. The costume started in Northern Germany where his ecclesiastic robe was shed for a simple one of fur and he was then called PELZE NICOL, or fur clad Nicholas.

Introduced 1993

$\mathcal{S}$ANTA CLAUS

USA
CIRCA 1915

This is one version of an American Santa of the early 1900's. It is somewhat similar to the 1920 chocolate mold Santa but has much more detail and adornment since it was inspired by Christmas post card art. The 1920 Santa is a simpler design because its origins are in chocolate molds. Chocolate molds carry less detailing in order to be functional. Too many sharply outlined features would make it difficult to remove the chocolate figure from the mold.

This is one example of the "All American" red, white and blue versions of Santa Claus prevalent in the first two decades of this century. See information on the 1918 Santa to find further history concerning red, white and blue Santas.

Introduced 1984

SINT NIKLAES

BELGIUM
CIRCA 1916

The inspiration for the design of this St. Nicholas was the art on several Christmas postcards from the same period. The figures were all dressed in white fur robes, white hat and white boots. The inscription on the front of one of the post cards reads "JOYEUX NOEL."

Except for the doll in his basket back-pack, all of the gifts are wrapped in pastel colors. The combination of white fur and pastel colors make him an elegant and charming version of the Belgian Sint Niklaes.

Introduced 1992

$\mathcal{J}$INT NIKLAES

BELGIUM
CIRCA 1917

Inspired by Belgian Christmas card art, the creator of this figure used a number of clues to ascertain the circa date.

The brown fabric coat appears to be of military style with its large, stand up collar. This and the toy bugles and toy gun hanging from his belt are hints that the art bears influence from World War I (1914 - 1918).

A brown-robed Sint Niklaes in Belgium or St. Nicholas in Germany was not uncommon, possibly because the earlier Pelze Nicol (Nicholas with Fur) was often depicted in brown fur.

Introduced 1989   Retired 1993

THE LITTLE ABC BOOK
McLoughlin Bros.
1884

$\mathcal{S}$ANTA CLAUS

USA
CIRCA 1918

This very elegant, somewhat patriotic Santa Claus with the blue pants and scarlet robe trimmed in white ermine is holding a brass toy sword. Metal toy swords were very popular with children at the time, as there seemed to be no thought of the dangers inherent in playing with them.

In the information on the 1912 Santa we mention that Thomas Nast created the first red, white and blue Uncle Sam Santa in 1863 Civil War surroundings. This 1912 version was starred and striped, as well as colored red, white and blue. The rosy cheeked 1918 Santa Claus, being more portly and jovial, and having red, white and blue coloration may be the epitome of the American Santa Claus we should adopt today!

Introduced 1991

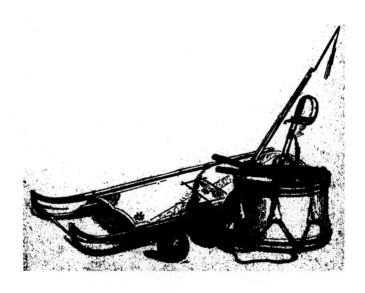

ST. NICHOLAS

CZECHOSLOVAKIA
CIRCA 1919

The Memories of Santa® circa 1919 figure was the result of combining several ideas from post cards by one artist of the same country and period into one composite to create this particular St. Nicholas of Czechoslovakia.

It illustrates graphically the customs and traditions of Christmas throughout the world. We have St. Nicholas, or Santa, with a hatchet in his pocket after cutting down the Christmas tree and a branch of holly in his arm, the evergreens symbolizing the perpetuation of life into the coming year. His back-pack is full of toys for the good boys and girls and the bag in his right hand holds apples and food for the poor and needy....

The idea of perpetuating life on earth, the love of children and gift giving, and charity to the poor and needy are all in the true spirit of Christmas.

Introduced 1988

SANTA CLAUS

AMERICA
CIRCA 1920

This very typical Santa from the twenties was inspired by a chocolate mold from the antique collection of the creator of the Memories of Santa™.

Incised in the metal mold is the name of the German mold manufacturer ANTON REICHE, DRESDEN (Germany) and the maker's item number, #114.

This particular Santa mold was made for the American market, judging from the short coat and hat. The more stern German St. Nicholas would have been dressed in a long hooded robe.

The Santa was colored red, white and blue in keeping with the Santa Claus art of this period.

Introduced by Christmas Reproductions, Inc. in 1983 as a limited edition (1920A), the design of this piece was altered in 1984 to protect the integrity of the first edition by placing a bear under Santa's right arm (1920B). The bear represented the famous "Teddy" bear, named after President Theodore Roosevelt, which was still a popular toy in the 1920's.

1920A Introduced 1983	Retired 1984
1920B Introduced 1984	Retired 1987

FATHER CHRISTMAS

ENGLAND
CIRCA 1922

In England Father Christmas was often depicted with a basket full of toys on a pull sled. Very unusual though, he is shown with a lavender robe. Purple and lavender were colors usually reserved for royalty. By doing this, the artist may be raising Father Christmas to royal status.

The picture of Father Christmas (opposite page) and the 1893 Santa Claus engraving below remind us that he used to bring children their Christmas trees along with their toys.

Introduced 1993

#

AMERICA
CIRCA 1925

Like the Circa 1920 Memories of Santa figure, this 1925 Santa was also inspired by an early chocolate mold. It was used by a German confectioner whose factory was in New Jersey. The metal mold itself had no marking but was most probably made in Germany.

Notice that this Santa is more plump than the 1920 chocolate mold Santa. This is indicative of the trend in the 1920's and 30's of the American artists and sculpturers to portray jolly old Santa as more weighty with round rosy cheeks.

Not represented on the chocolate mold, typical toys of the era were added to the bag of the Santa figure, as he now was evolving closer to the current day Santa Claus.

Introduced by Christmas Reproductions, Inc. in 1983 as a limited edition (1925A), the design of this piece was altered in 1984 to protect the integrity of the first edition by changing the bear in Santa's bag to a doll (1925B).

1925A Introduced 1983	Retired 1984
1925B Introduced 1984	Retired 1987

CELLULOID SANTA CLAUS
BUTLER BROS. CATALOGUE
1925

$\mathcal{S}$ANTA CLAUS

AMERICA
CIRCA 1926

This Santa's costume is of the style most often used in the 1920's magazine illustrations. The bag on his back is decorated with a mystic crescent moon and stars on a blue background, used more than once during this period. Possibly this was inspired by St. Nicholas' Middle-Eastern origin.

The finger pointing to his nose was taken from Clement C. Moore's "A Visit from St. Nicholas" where he wrote:

"And laying his finger aside of his nose,

And giving a nod, up the chimney he rose;

He sprang to his sleigh, to his team gave a whistle,

And away they all flew like the down of a thistle;

But I heard him exclaim, ere he drove out of sight,

'HAPPY CHRISTMAS TO ALL, AND TO ALL A GOOD NIGHT.'"

Introduced 1990

$\mathcal{V}$OLUNTEERS of AMERICA SANTA

AMERICA
CIRCA 1933

The Volunteers of America organization adopted Santa Claus to spearhead their campaign to raise funds for the poor and needy. This yearly campaign was started by the Volunteers of America during the depression and continues to this day. It is an important chapter in the life and legend of Santa Claus.

What better personality could they have selected than Santa Claus, who is known by all mankind to be charitable and kind to the needy? His reputation for charity began in the third century when Nicholas was still a boy in the town of Patura in the country of Lycia, now a small part of Turkey. Here he placed three bags of gold through the window of the home of a needy family.

Later in the 13th century the Nuns in France began leaving presents at the homes of the poor on the eve of Nicholas' Day, December 5th. This custom spread across Europe and street parades were led by someone representing St. Nicholas mounted on a white horse.

Introduced 1990

Soda Pop Santa

America
Circa 1938

The modern Santa Claus, "chubby and plump, with cheeks like roses and a nose like a cherry" began in the 1920's with artists such as Norman Rockwell and Linedecker. In December 1926, the Saturday Evening Post published such a Santa by Norman Rockwell on the front cover. The same magazine ran on the cover of the December 26, 1925 issue a Linedecker painting of a Santa Claus with similar characteristics. Both artists were published often during this magazine-reading era in America.

In 1931 Coca-Cola first commissioned Haddon Sundblom to portray his version of Santa for their Christmas advertising campaign. He too created a plump and chubby Santa with rosy cheeks and nose. The Coke ads appeared on billboards and magazines and reached millions of people. Other soda-pop makers commissioned other artists to carry out similar ad campaigns.

Through the tremendous exposure of these advertising campaigns the Soda-Pop Santa became the most popular Santa ever in America.

Introduced 1989   Retired 1993

CHRISTMAS SAVINGS CLUB
SANTA

AMERICA
CIRCA 1940

The Memories of Santa Collection™ would not be complete without a reproduction of the Savings Bank Christmas Club Santa which was very popular in the 1930's and 1940's.

As a premium for joining the Christmas Club, banks often offered a cardboard die-cut Santa Claus for hanging on the Christmas tree.

The reverse side of the cardboard Santa (see reproduction below) was imprinted with details and "benefits" of joining the club. You will notice the bank was allowing the customer to deposit their savings without interest.

Introduced 1992

CHRISTKINDL MARKET
depicted on a
CHOCOLATE MOLD
circa 1870

CIRCA DATE	DESCRIPTION	COUNTRY OF ORIGIN	RELEASED	RETIRED
1840	St. Nick by T.C. Boyd	USA	1993	
1850	Weihnachtsman (Christmas Man)	GERMANY	1983	1987
1867	Santa Claus by C. Bush	USA	1991	
1872	Santa Claus by Thomas Nast	USA	1985	1992
1880	Ashenclos (Nicholas with Ashes)	GERMANY	1983	1987
1885	Kris Kringle	USA	1985	1992
1888	Father Christmas with Wassail Bowl	ENGLAND	1988	
1889	St. Nicholas with Doll	GERMANY	1990	
1890	Pelze Nicol	NO. GERMANY	1983	1987
1890	Santa Claus by Puck Magazine	USA	1990	
1893	Weihnachtsman (Christmas Man)	GERMANY	1992	
1894	Niklo	AUSTRIA	1987	
1895	Kris Kringle Pennsylvania	USA	1984	1987
1896	St. Nicholas	CZECHOSLOVAKIA	1992	
1897	St. Nicholas	CZECHOSLOVAKIA	1987	
1898	Hello Santa	USA	1993	
1899	Santa Claus by R. Tuck & Sons	USA	1991	
1900	Sint Niklaes	BELGIUM	1988	
1901	Pelze Nicol	GERMANY	1987	
1902	Pere Noel	FRANCE	1988	
1903	Father Christmas	RUSSIA	1989	1993
1904	St. Nicholas	GERMANY	1989	1991
1905	Father Christmas	GREAT BRITAIN	1984	1990
1906	St. Nicholas	BAVARIA	1987	
1907	Sinterklass	HOLLAND	1986	1991
1908	Buller Clos (Nicholas with Bells)	NO. GERMANY	1986	1991
1909	Weihnachtsman	SO. GERMANY	1985	1992
1910	Sint Niklaes	BELGIUM	1985	1992
1911	St. Nicholas	GERMANY	1989	1993
1912	Uncle Sam Santa	USA	1986	1991
1913	Tomta	SWEDEN	1991	
1914	Vive St. Nicholas	BELGIUM	1993	
1915	Santa Claus	USA	1984	1990
1916	Sint Niklaes	BELGIUM	1992	
1917	Sint Niklaes	BELGIUM	1989	1993
1918	Santa Claus	USA	1991	
1919	St. Nicholas	CZECHOSLOVAKIA	1988	
1920	Santa Claus	USA	1983	1990
1922	Father Christmas	ENGLAND	1993	
1925	Santa Claus	USA	1983	1990
1926	Santa Claus	USA	1990	
1933	Volunteers of America Santa Claus	USA	1990	
1938	Soda Pop Santa	USA	1989	1993
1940	Christmas Savings Club Santa	USA	1992	

$\mathcal{T}$HE MANY NAMES OF SANTA CLAUS

ASHENCLOS (Nicholas carrying Ashes)	N. GERMANY
BABBO NATALE (Santa Claus)	ITALY
BESANA	ITALY
BULLER CLOS (Nicholas with Bells)	N. GERMANY
DUN CHE LAD REN (Christmas Old Man)	CHINA
FATHER CHRISTMAS	GREAT BRITAIN
FATHER CHRISTMAS (Before the 1917 Revolution)	RUSSIA
GRANDFATHER FROST (After the 1917 Revolution)	RUSSIA
KRIS KRINGLE (Santa Claus)	PENNSYLVANIA, USA
NIKLO (St. Nicholas)	AUSTRIA
NIKOLAI CHOODOVORITZ (Nicholas Miracle Maker)	RUSSIA
PELZE NICOL (Fur-clad Nicholas)	N. GERMANY
PERE NOEL (Father Christmas)	FRANCE
SAINT A. CLAUS (St. Nicholas)	NEW AMSTERDAM, USA
SAMIKLOS (St. Nicholas)	SWITZERLAND
SAN NICOLA (St. Nicholas)	ITALY
SANT NIKOLAUS (St. Nicholas)	SWITZERLAND
SANCTE CLAUS (St. Nicholas)	NEW AMSTERDAM, USA
SANTA CLAUS (St. Nicholas)	NEW YORK, USA
SANTIKLOS (St. Nicholas)	SWITZERLAND
SCHIMMELREITER (Nicholas on White Horse)	GERMANY
SINT NIKLAES (St. Nicholas)	BELGIUM
SINTERKLASS (St. Nicholas)	HOLLAND
SVENTY NICKOLY (St. Nicholas)	POLAND
SZENT NICHOLAZ (St. Nicholas)	HUNGARY
TELAPO MIKULAS (Santa Claus)	HUNGARY
THE HOLY MAN	TYROL
TOMTA (Santa Claus)	SWEDEN
WEIHNACHTSMAN (Christmas Man)	GERMANY

$\mathcal{H}$ISTORICAL ACCURACY
and the MEMORIES of SANTA COLLECTION™

Christmas Reproductions, Inc. certifies that the circa dates on each of its Santas in the Memories of Santa Collection have been carefully researched and documented as accurately as possible. The word circa is defined as "about," or "approximately." This terminology (circa) is used on all Santas even though some of the figures in the collection have exact dates, discerned from the antique art which was the source for the figure. Exact dates are derived from postmarks and dates on magazines, newspapers, and other periodicals.

If antique post cards and chromolithographs do not have a postmark or date, we research any logo or trademark to ascertain when the printer was in business. If dates cannot be determined by these methods or if we require more information regarding date or country of origin we then study the style of dress of the people (usually children) in a particular piece of art to determine the time period and sometimes the country of origin.

There are times that analyzing the artifacts in the pictures helps us determine dates and the country of origin. An example of this is the 1898 HELLO SANTA figure, where we created a composite from several newspaper drawings of Nast-like Santas of this period. Since the telephone was often used with Santa in the late 1800's we chose to show him holding a "Desk Set" phone instead of a crank style wall phone, which would be difficult to represent with a free-standing Santa. We then looked up the history of the telephone in the local library and found the Desk Set phone was first introduced in 1897. Thus, we knew we could date the Santa circa 1898. If we had used the wall phone as shown on the information page of the 1898 Santa the date would have to have been 1884.

$\mathcal{A}$BOUT THE AUTHOR

Don Warning was born and raised in Dayton, Ohio, as a member of a family who considered Christmas not just a day, but a season, starting at Thanksgiving and not officially ending until January 5, the feast of the three kings.

His father and mother, second and third generation German-Americans, imparted all the love and tradition of Christmas to him and his sister Dorothy. The family made most of their own ornaments, trimmings, and trappings for indoors and out, and baked copious amounts of Christmas goodies every year.

After high school and two years in the Army he entered the University of Dayton, and after graduation became a buyer of Christmas decorations and toys for the Finke Co., a wholesale distributor in Dayton. After several years he started his own sales rep company covering Ohio, Kentucky, Indiana, and Michigan, specializing in Christmas Decorations. Three years later he moved his family to New York to become National Sales Manager and Marketing Vice President for a major Christmas manufacturer.

After nine years the company was taken over in a corporate buyout and Warning resigned. He then started his own sales representative company in New York called Christmas Eve, Inc. The Christmas Eve name was conceived to illustrate to the trade that the word EVE suggests all the busy planning and preparation required for the holiday itself, similar to and perhaps inspired by his early family Christmas experiences.

While a junior in College he married his wife Mary and they started their family of (now) eight children, five girls and three boys. The family lived in an 1850 farm house in Bellbrook, Ohio. In searching for antique and victorian furniture for the house Don began to collect antique Christmas decorations and artifacts. The collecting continued and expanded when the family moved to New York.

In his office Warning displayed his collection of 65 antique chocolate molds, mostly Santa Clauses. By arranging these Santas in order, from the early St. Nicholases to the Santa molds of the 1920's and 1930's, he could see the evolution of the early St. Nicholas to the current day American Santa. Thus began the seeds of development of the Memories of Santa Collection™, telling the Santa Claus story chronologically.

Warning could not find a manufacturer or importer he thought would understand or undertake this project and decided to start a new company on his own to manufacture the Santa collection. He called it Christmas Reproductions, Inc., his own company devoted to the reproduction of Christmas antiques to preserve the traditions and the customs of Christmases past.

The research and designing of the first Memories of Santa® pieces were done in 1982, one year after Christmas Eve was formed, then Christmas Reproductions, Inc. was incorporated and the first five Santas were introduced to the trade in 1983. The initial Santas were influenced by the details of Warning's collection of antique chocolate molds. Since then, various antique memorabilia were used as inspiration for the sculptures, including early chromolithographs, old post cards, antique trading cards, magazines, newspapers, books, calendars, and the like.

Each year the collection consists of 24 hand-painted earthenware Santas representing different countries at various periods of time and each year Christmas Reproductions, Inc. adds four new Santas to the line and retires four Santas.

The Memories of Santa Collection has now become a very important Christmas collectible, complete with legends, history and circa dates, all historically documented.

From 1983 to 1993 Christmas Reproductions, Inc. will have designed and produced forty-four Santas for the collection.

"MERRY CHRISTMAS TO ALL, AND TO ALL
A GOOD-NIGHT!"